IRELAND'S

Hidden Depths

A Sherkin Island Marine Station Publication | Paul Kay

This book is dedicated to Paul's wife Lucy and to his mother Norma.

Published by Sherkin Island Marine Station, Sherkin Island, Co. Cork, Ireland.
www.sherkinmarine.ie

Photography & text by Paul Kay (except those by Lucy Kay – the image on page 19, the lower images on pages 108 and 132, the inset images on pages 10, 30 and 46 and the image of Paul Kay on back cover fold).

Typeset & layout by Susan Murphy Wickens

Printed by City Print Ltd, Victoria Cross, Cork, Ireland.

ISBN: 978-1-870492-53-9

We would like to acknowledge the help and assistance of the following: Lucy Kay, Lin Baldock, Francis Bunker, Bernard Picton, Paul Brazier, Rohan Holt, Mike Guiry and Nuala Norris. Thank you to the members of An Coiste Téarmaíochta (The Terminology Committee of Foras na Gaeilge), particularly Jenny Ní Chumhaill and Máire Nic Mheanman, for their wonderful assistance with the Irish names.

The names of many marine animals vary, so in the book the most common English name (capitalised and in bold) has been used followed by the more definitive scientific name (italicised) and then the Irish name (in grey). In some cases animals may actually still not have common names.

Image on right: Jewel Anemones

Contents

Foreword

Here in Ireland we laud the wonders of our lakes, rivers, forests, mountains, and the flora and fauna, yet around us we have equal wonders in the seas that lap our shores. Hidden by depths of water and rarely in view, it is not surprising that less is made of the life beneath the waves. Few people, other than scuba divers, have the privilege of seeing the vast array of underwater species of animals and plants; fewer still photograph this hidden world. However, with this book we are fortunate that the gifted Paul Kay, who has spent 30 years photographing the underwater flora and fauna in the waters around Ireland and Great Britain, is helping to share this world with everyone.

Matt Murphy, Director,
Sherkin Island Marine Station

Paul came to our marine station at Sherkin Island as a volunteer photographer to record the built heritage of the islands of Roaringwater Bay in 1981. He was enthused by the then volunteer scuba divers at the Station who talked of what they saw under the waves. When he returned home to the UK he took up scuba diving and invested in underwater photographic equipment. Since then he has written many books and magazine articles, all enhanced by photographs taken during the many hours he has spent exploring the marine environment, in what can only be described as a labour of love.

The marine station in its 35 years of existence has had, as one of its goals, the education of people about the commercial and environmental importance of our seas. With this in mind, we have decided to publish this book. Paul Kay's fine photographs and accompanying text highlights just a fraction of the many thousands of animals and plants that live in the waters around our coast. We hope that they will give the reader a new perspective on the sea, and encourage a sustained interest in its wonder and potential.

Matt Murphy, Director,
Sherkin Island Marine Station

Introduction

Introducing a book about Ireland's undersea world is difficult. For most people it remains a largely unknown world, perhaps fleetingly glimpsed in television programmes, sometimes mentioned on the radio or occasionally shown in magazines. It is only seen directly by the fortunate few who are able to scuba dive and visit it for themselves.

It is nearly 20 years since Matt Murphy first published "Ireland's Marine Life, a World of Beauty" which showed off Ireland's rich and spectacular undersea world and its inhabitants. Since then, many thousands of copies have been sold. In the intervening, years technology has progressed and has profoundly altered underwater photography, with digital imaging having rapidly taken over from film.

It would be marvellous if our understanding of, and care for, the marine environment had also progressed at such a rate. Unfortunately, accessing the undersea world around Ireland still remains the difficult and often physically challenging affair that it has been since scuba diving became viable. There have been changes though, and now there are several marine aquaria around Ireland's coast where some of the sea's inhabitants can be seen alive and in conditions similar to those in which they would normally live. Yet photographic images, either moving or still, remain the only medium through which most people see the underwater marine environment, even now in the twenty-first century.

I realised a long time ago that I was extremely privileged to be able to explore the undersea world directly for myself. When I first visited Sherkin Island, in Co. Cork as a volunteer, I had no idea that it would be a life-changing experience and that my life's course would be irrevocably altered. I was, and still am, fascinated by the creatures that I saw on the shore, in the station's aquaria and underwater. Back in the early eighties, underwater photography was difficult and frustrating; producing

Cape Clear Island from the Marine Station.

A rocky reef off the Ring of Kerry.

Maerl and boulder seabed off Connemara.

a satisfying image was something of a triumph. Nevertheless, this book contains several images from those times which, whilst not of the technical standard produced by today's marvellous digital cameras, are now something of a historic record in underwater photography terms.

Having spent several seasons at the Marine Station and having revisited in the years that followed, I was delighted when Matt decided to produce his first book on Ireland's Marine Life. Since then my enthusiasm for the stunningly beautiful scenery, fascinating wildlife and glorious undersea forests to be found in the shallow waters around the Irish coast has remained as strong as ever, and together with my wife Lucy, I have visited and continue to visit other parts of Ireland, diving whenever and wherever I am able to.

Ireland has an immensely diverse marine environment, with massive variations in both the shallow coastal seabeds and their inhabitants. The undersea off the coast changes just as much as the coast itself. Matt's decision to produce a second book on Ireland's marine environment means that it is now possible to show the richness with the benefit of new technologies, which enable it to be seen better than was possible with the first book.

Any book on the marine environment has to be selective and needs to be laid out in some sort of order. Matt's daughter, Susan, is responsible for the clean and simple design and layout. Together, we have tried to place the creatures included in the book in a coherent, if not strictly scientific order. Rather than write pages and pages of facts about the plants and animals, I have simply captioned them with what I hope are interesting snippets of information.

No attempt has been made to explain Ireland's highly complex undersea environment in scientific terms. There are numerous books and plenty of scientific papers which do that – at least up to the point where our knowledge currently stops. We still have a great deal more to learn about the sea and its inhabitants. This book is simply intended to show just a few of the facets of the life found in the shallow seas around the Irish coast.

The images shown span some 30 years of underwater photography and were all taken at locations around the Irish coast. Some undoubtedly show their age but are included because they illustrate important points. Having recently revisited some of the sites where I first dived back in the early eighties, I am also aware that the photographs are actually very valuable as an archive and allow comparison with the same places today and in the future. In many cases, there are slight differences as encrusting creatures have grown or disappeared or been replaced. On the whole, though, the differences are trivial and similar species can still be found where we first photographed them.

Today the need for long-term information about the seas and their inhabitants has never been greater, so any underwater images from decades ago can now be of scientific use. As I originally trained as a scientific photographer, this means that I have almost returned to my roots – although not in a way that I might ever have anticipated.

I do need to thank many people for their help in producing this publication. Matt Murphy, the instigator of the book, who of course is as enthusiastic as ever about his Marine Station and everything to do with it and Ireland's environment; Susan Murphy Wickens for her design, editing skills and patience; Lin Baldock and my wife Lucy Kay for reading and commenting on the text. Lucy also dived with me at many of the locations shown and has kindly allowed me to use of some of her photographs.

Paul Kay

An undersea canyon off Sherkin Island.

Anemones
& Relatives

Even a casual observer of rockpools will probably have seen an anemone, even if it just resembles a blob of shiny, rubbery jelly stuck on the rock. There are far more anemones than the few found on the shore, which are not seen at their best. Anemones, along with their relatives – corals, sea fans, sea pens, jellyfish and more – are a colourful and often beautiful group of animals.

Whilst many are composed entirely of soft tissues, others have hard skeletons which remain after they die. Some are solitary whilst others form vast colonies or live together in huge numbers.

Our experience of rockpool anemones might well mislead us into thinking that these animals are mostly found on rocky seabeds, whereas in fact some are perfectly adapted to a life in sand or even soft mud. Most anemones live fixed in place but some can and do move, albeit slowly. The largest anemones found in Irish waters can be as much as 30 cm high whilst the smallest are just a few millimetres in diameter.

Jellyfish may not at first appear to be related to anemones but they are and some do exhibit similar behaviour. Stalked jellies actually live attached to seaweed for example, something which may be surprising and which we may not consider very jellyfish-like. In short, anemones and their relatives are complex and diverse.

DAHLIA ANEMONE
Urticina felina • Bundún leice dáilia

The Dahlia Anemone is actually quite a common anemone but is only seen by those who are prepared to look for it in deep pools (generally pools at the bottom of the shore), and by those who can actually penetrate the undersea world for themselves.

Soft Corals

DEAD MEN'S FINGERS
Alcyonium digitatum • Méara mara

Dead Men's Fingers are soft corals which form bulbous white, yellow or orange masses and whose shape aptly fits their name. They are colonies made up of numerous individuals, each known as a polyp, which can expand and contract like a small anemone. They favour locations which can experience quite strong current flows; the polyps will extend out into the current to capture edible morsels as they sweep past.

RED FINGERS
Alcyonium glomeratum • Méara mara dearga

Red Fingers are a closely related species, which are found on Ireland's Atlantic coasts. Their overall colour is, as their name suggests, red (with distinctly white polyps) rather than the white, yellow or orange of their relatives, and they are far less common.

Soft corals cannot build reefs because they have no skeleton and it is the skeletons from vast numbers of hard corals which actually form tropical coral reefs. Dead Men's Fingers favour bedrock or large boulders to live on and can be found on vertical surfaces as well as on flatter or ridged areas. Here, expanded polyps are being buffeted by the current.

Delicate Beauties

JEWEL ANEMONE
Corynactis viridis • **Bundún leice na séad**

Jewel Anemones are small and often brightly coloured anemones. They are highly variable in colour and often make up for their small size (usually around a centimetre in diameter) by occurring in vast numbers. In the right conditions they can be extremely prolific and may cover many square metres of rock.

Areas of rock can be completely covered with anemones of one colour variation, whilst adjacent areas are covered in others of quite a different colour. This is because the anemones of a similar colour are all clones from one anemone and each one has been formed by splitting away from another identical anemone.

This can be appreciated at the offshore sites where Jewel Anemones can be extremely prolific. These include such places as the Fastnet Rock, off the West Cork coast, and Inishbofin, off the west coast of Co. Galway (which is where this photograph was taken). In the photograph a larger sheet of light green anemones has enclosed an area of reddish ones.

The orange masses are Dead Men's Fingers with their polyps closed up, and like their soft coral cousins, Jewel Anemones, they not only withstand harsh conditions but actually thrive in them. So this small delicate creature is considerably more robust that it might at first appear.

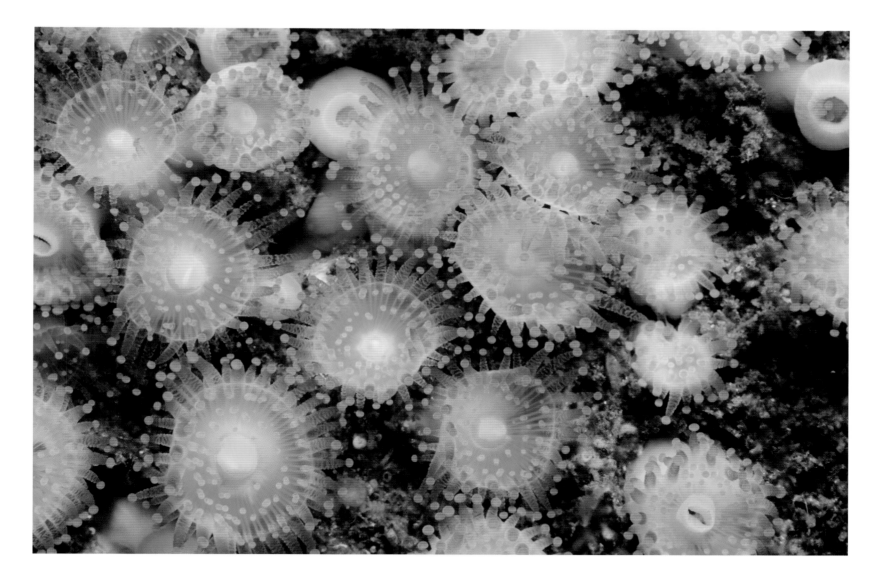

When viewed in close up, Jewel Anemones reveal themselves to be intricate, highly coloured and very beautiful little creatures. They are easy to identify as their tentacles end in a small knobble, unlike any other anemones found around the Irish coast, although like other anemones, they can retract their tentacles and contract to become a rounded blob.

Flowery Animals

DAHLIA ANEMONE
Urticina felina • Bundún leice dáilia

One of the larger anemones found around the Irish coastline is the Dahlia Anemone. The largest specimens are actually found in deep rockpools on the lower shore, but are more common below the tide zone. Smaller ones can sometimes be found higher up on the shore, as far as the mid-tide line.

These anemones can measure up to 15 cm in diameter and may be very abundant. They especially like living in the bottom of crevices and rocky gullies and these can sometimes be completely carpeted with them.

Dahlia Anemones are patterned but the clarity of the pattern depends on the colours of each anemone, which can vary considerably. Some show rather indistinct patterns whilst others, with contrasting colours, have very clear patterning.

This photograph shows several Dahlias sharing, or more accurately, competing for space with vast numbers of small brittlestars in an area of high water movement – conditions favoured by both of these creatures. The water carries a lot of suspended particulate matter making it turbid and murky; consequently the dull light and low contrast results in poor visibility. However, to the creatures that live here the turbidity means a lot of food is available and the seabed is absolutely crammed with animals as a result.

Sometimes Dahlia Anemones will attach themselves to near-vertical surfaces, and blue-green water provides a colourful backdrop when looking upwards. This photograph is deceptive as it is actually a view taken looking up a steep rock wall. Here the Dahlia Anemone is surrounded by slightly-curled up Feather Stars (see page 58) and many encrusting creatures.

DAHLIA ANEMONE • *Urticina felina* • **Bundún leice dáilia**

Patterning and colour of some anemones, such as the Dahlia, can be very variable; yet there are some colours and patterns which appear to be repeated sporadically – this is one of them. It was photographed on a ledge on the south coast of the Aran Island of Inis Mór, on the west coast of Ireland.

ELEGANT ANEMONE • *Sagartia elegans* var. *rosea* • **Bundún leice faithneach**

There is little truly 'bare' rock underwater; it is found only where currents are so strong that nothing can withstand them. Most rock is as in this photograph – absolutely covered in marine life, including colourful animals such as these two pretty Elegant Anemones.

Unusually Abundant

FRIED EGG or SANDALLED ANEMONE
Actinothöe sphyrodeta • Bundún nóinín mór

Nestling amidst dead men's fingers and light-bulb sea squirts in the photograph to the left, is an anemone. One of this anemone's common names is the Fried Egg Anemone and, although this one is white, these anemones often have a yellow centre and so are thought to resemble fried eggs.

This is a pretty little anemone and might appear to be far too fragile to survive in anything but the calmest of water. In actual fact this creature, like many other small anemones, really thrives in exposed locations with substantial water flows and strong currents. It lives on rocky seabeds, generally favouring gently sloping to vertical surfaces.

When it contracts, a pattern of fine vertical lines can be seen on the column of its body. Such lines are visible on some of the anemones in the photograph on the opposite page.

Up to 100 shortish, untidy and spiky tentacles are characteristic of this anemone.

Large numbers of Fried Egg Anemones (seen in this photograph taken just off Achill Island, off the Co. Mayo coast) are relatively unusual, as the anemone is more often seen in much smaller numbers. In between the anemones, the rock is also covered in calcareous algae and encrusting animals, with no bare rock visible at all.

DEVONSHIRE CUP CORAL • *Caryophyllia smithii* • Coiréalach cupach

Although Ireland has no inshore coral reefs like those in the tropics, there are corals here which do have a skeleton. The Devonshire Cup Coral is one and, although small (~1.5 cm diameter is typical), it is as colourful as any coral found in the tropics. As a solitary creature however, it cannot build reefs.

PLUMOSE ANEMONE • *Metridium senile* • Bláth mara

Plumose anemones are often associated with wrecks and man-made structures. They can coat a wreck so densely that it turns white and becomes somewhat ghostly in appearance. However, they usually live on bedrock and boulders where they are easily recognised by their feathery tentacles.

BEADLET ANEMONE • *Actinia equina* • **Bundún coirníneach**

One of the best known of the anemones is the Beadlet. Most people see it on the shore fastened to rocks at low tide where it often resembles a jelly-like 'blob', but underwater with its tentacles expanded it looks completely different.

The Climbing Anemone

SNAKELOCKS ANEMONE
Anemonia viridis • Bundún nathairiúil

Snakelocks anemones often climb up seaweeds and seagrass to be nearer the surface and bathed in as much light as possible. This is because the anemone's cells contain symbiotic algae called zooxanthellae and it is the chlorophyll in these algae which gives the anemone its overall greenish colouration. The anemone benefits from having the algae in its cells and as the algae (being plants) need light, the anemone tries to live in very brightly lit places, preferably in shallow water.

A Sun Worshipper

Although Snakelocks Anemones are often drab looking, some do have more colourful markings. Many of these have vivid green tentacles with purple tips but a few show red and green striped tentacles.

Scientists have found that the anemone's brighter colouration is partly due to the presence of fluorescent proteins, which may help to protect it from the ultraviolet radiation present in daylight. So its rather sophisticated colouring might just prevent this sun-worshipping anemone from getting sunburnt! These proteins also have exciting possibilities, due to their technical properties. They may prove useful in a variety of fields, including high-resolution microscopy and perhaps even in digital data storage.

Sand & Gravel

IMPERIAL ANEMONE
Aureliania heterocera • **Bundún leice impiriúil**

There are many anemones which live in gravel, sand and mud. Of these, the Imperial Anemone can be one of the more colourful ones, and may be red, orange and yellow, as well as white. It has extremely short tentacles and, at first glance, may even appear to have been flattened.

This anemone is found on what is often referred to as 'mixed ground', which consists of a pebble, gravel and sand mix and is usually found singly rather than in numbers or small groups. Its not a very common anemone but is found in Irish waters where the seabed is suitable. It retracts into the seabed with surprising speed if disturbed.

Seen in the Dark

NIGHT ANEMONE
Halcampoides elongatus • **Bundún oíche**

This is a burrowing anemone whose tentacles can span up to 15 cm. It is widely distributed around the world and is found at great depths too – down to at least 1000 m. It can be seen in shallow water (at night) in just a few locations in Ireland, so it is thought to be extremely rare here. It is shown here in a maerl bed in Kilkieran Bay in Galway, in an area that is swept by tidal currents and at a depth of around 10 m.

This anemone is actually nocturnal. Few divers dive at night in the areas in which it is found, which might well help explain why it is seldom seen or recorded.

RED-SPECKLED ANEMONE • *Anthopleura ballii* • Bundún deargbhreactha

Although apparently living in gravel (or in maerl as seen here), this pretty anemone will actually be fastened onto a solid, buried object, such as a rock or shell. It is found around the south and western coasts of Ireland.

Beauty in the Mud

FIREWORKS ANEMONE
Pachycerianthus multiplicatus • **Bundún tine ealaíne**

Firework Anemones are the largest anemones found in Ireland and can measure up to 30 cm high whilst their span of around 200 tentacles can also be 30 cm in diameter. They have been found in depths of as little as 10 m of water, and down as far as 130 m. These beautiful creatures do require rather unusual conditions though. This is because they live in a mucus-lined tube, which is buried in mud, and as they are very large anemones, the tube has to be up to a metre long. They require a relatively sheltered environment with soft mud, which is thick enough to accommodate such a length of tube.

The mud also has to be stable and be swept by light currents. Few places around the Irish coast are able to offer such conditions, so this means that the anemone is comparatively rare in Ireland, where it has been found in water depths of 10 to 50 m.

In fact suitable habitats are more common in the sea lochs on the western coast of Scotland, where the anemones are often found alongside other typical sea loch dwelling species, such as sea pens. Whilst Connemara, in the West of Ireland, has no sea lochs, it does have some locations that offer similar conditions to those found in the Scottish sea lochs. Consequently, Fireworks Anemones are found there and that is where these photographs were taken. Sea pens can be seen in the top left-hand of the photograph, above the Fireworks Anemone.

Anemones such as the Fireworks Anemone extend their long tentacles into the water to trap any small edible material which drifts past. Large specimens of these anemones are unmistakable. Smaller ones might be mistaken for other mud-dwelling anemones, such as the burrowing anemone (*Cerianthus lloydii*), although their striped tentacles are usually sufficient to identify them.

The mud in which the anemones live does not swirl around in the relatively still conditions in which they thrive. It can be so stable that an easily-visible, brownish algal mat may develop on the surface of the mud, as can be seen in the top photograph. This can only happen if the mud is not stirred up and illustrates that the water movement around the anemones is gentle, although clearly sufficient enough to supply them with the food that they require.

When the tentacles catch food or if they are disturbed, fireworks anemones react in a determined rather than rapid manner and the tentacles curl up and roll in towards their central mouth with clear deliberation. Sometimes a crab will be seen hiding alongside the anemone's column (as its body is known) and must enjoy protection from the anemone's substantial stinging tentacles.

Not Quite a Jellyfish

COMMON OR MOON JELLYFISH (Scyphistomae)
Aurelia aurita • Smugairle róin coiteann (Scifiostóma)

These small anemone-like creatures are polyps called Scyphistomae and are the second stage of the life cycle of the Moon Jellyfish. The polyps settle onto rock. They favour overhung vertical surfaces, where they survive over winter until very early spring. Then they release ephyrae (another stage in the Moon Jellyfish's life cycle), which finally develop into the larger, more familiar bell-shaped medusae.

Jellyfish Smack

COMMON OR MOON JELLYFISH
Aurelia aurita • Smugairle róin coiteann

Moon Jellyfish can occur in huge swarms and when they do, they are referred to as 'smacks' of jellyfish. These jellyfish eat the planktonic stages of numerous other marine organisms. In turn, they are eaten by other animals, including Sunfish and Leatherback Turtles. Both the latter can be found in Irish waters, although it is fairly unusual to see a Sunfish and sightings of Leatherback Turtles are rare.

COMPASS JELLYFISH • *Chrysaora hysoscella* • Smugairle an chompáis

Small fishes can live amongst the stinging tentacles of jellyfish. Here, safe from many predators, two small whiting swim amongst the protective tentacles of a Compass Jellyfish.

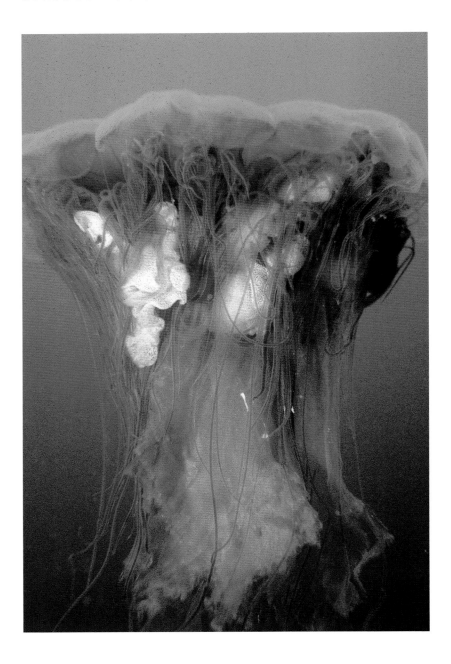

Colourful Stingers

BLUE or BLUEFISH JELLYFISH
Cyanea lamarkii • Smugairle róin gorm

This is the smaller relative of the Lion's Mane Jellyfish (*Cyanea capilliata*) which is also found in Irish seas. It is blue or yellow as opposed to the purple, brown or orange of its larger cousin.

Both of these jellyfish can inflict stings that generally cause only localised pain and soreness. People's susceptibility does vary significantly though, and whilst some may not even notice a sting, others can be badly affected and, in extreme and very rare cases, may even suffer from anaphylactic shock. Since this jellyfish is one of the known stingers it is probably best to avoid touching it. Even when it is washed up on a strandline, dead or dying it may still deliver a sting.

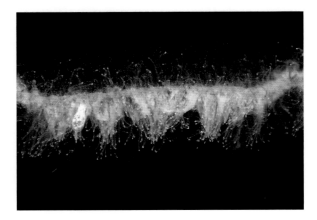

STRING JELLYFISH or PEARL-CHAIN JELLYFISH
Apolemia uvaria • Smugairle róin sreangánach

This weird creature is called a String Jelly or Pearl-chain Jellyfish. It is not really a jellyfish at all, but a colonial animal called a siphonophore. Like a jellyfish, it too can sting.

STALKED JELLYFISH • *Haliclystus auricula* • Smugairle róin gasach

We tend to think of jellyfish as floating creatures at the mercy of currents, waves and wind. Stalked Jellyfish, however, sway in unison with the seaweed and seagrass on which they live.

Crabs
& Relatives

C rabs are crustaceans – a group of animals with hard outer shells which also includes barnacles, shrimps, prawns, crawfish (or rock lobsters as they are sometimes known) and lobsters. With the exception of barnacles, most of these creatures are probably familiar because they include species that are edible and are considered to be somewhat expensive delicacies.

Lobsters and Scampi are both well-known to diners, but they have smaller, less well-known relatives like the Squat Lobsters. Crabs too are appreciated for their flavour but generally the crab served here in Ireland is the Edible Crab. Most smaller swimming, spider, and hermit crabs are considered too small to be viable as food and so are generally left alone. Both the Spiny Spider Crab and Velvet Swimming Crab are fished for but are usually shipped to France and Spain.

All these creatures are complex animals with some fascinating abilities. They can re-grow lost limbs for example, something which is very useful if a predator grabs a leg or when there are disputes over territory that lead to fighting. As they grow they shed their hard outer covering, revealing an identical soft version inside. This will expand to a larger size and then harden, so these animals literally grow in discrete 'steps'.

Different crustaceans adopt different strategies for survival. Some live in rocky areas and hide in crevices, some bury themselves under sand with just their eyes peering out, others use discarded shells as protection. A few even camouflage themselves by deliberately cultivating encrusting creatures all over their bodies.

SPINY SPIDER CRAB
Maja squinado • **Portán faoilinne spíonach**

The largest spider crab in Irish waters is this one – the Spiny Spider Crab – which is just taking up a defensive posture by raising its clawed arms in warning.

Careful Eater

SPINY SPIDER CRAB
Maja squinado • **Portán faoilinne spíonach**

Spiny Spider Crabs are the largest crab found around the Irish coast. Their bodies can reach approximately 20 cm in diameter, whilst their longest legs may be up to 50 cm in length.

These crabs seem to have become much more common over the last few decades. Apparently they cannot withstand prolonged cold and their population may have crashed after the severe winter of 1963. However, over the last few decades their numbers have been increasing and they are more abundant, even in the north, than they had been.

Despite having long, clawed arms, Spiny Spider Crabs are graceful eaters, plucking up tasty morsels and carefully transferring these to their mouth parts.

These crabs are commercially fished for, with most being exported to mainland Europe.

Soft, muddy seabeds have their disadvantages as they stir up all too easily and visibility then rapidly decreases.

Most seabeds seem acceptable to the Spiny Spider Crab. The one seen here on a rocky outcrop, next to a massive Boring Sponge, is surrounded by Dead Men's Fingers. They are good climbers and can clamber up surprisingly steep slopes. They can also be found on mud, sand, gravel and maerl seabeds.

Protected & Protecting

SPONGE or SCORPION SPIDER CRAB
Inachus sp. • Portán faoilinne scairpe

Two small spidery looking crabs, which are often covered in sponges, share the same common names in Ireland – although neither is known by the name given to similar crabs in the tropics, which is Decorator Crab. This name actually describes them very well, because they decorate themselves by fastening sponges all over their bodies, which not only survive, but grow and act as camouflage. Although here the yellow sponge actually makes the crab look rather more conspicuous as it clambers across dark seaweed!

These crabs can sometimes be found hiding under, or even in, the tentacles of various anemones which clearly do not sting them. The anemone provides protection for the crab, and presumably the crab may help prevent predators attacking the anemone.

Camouflage is less relevant when sheltering beneath an anemone's stinging tentacles for protection.

WRINKLED SWIMMING CRAB • *Liocarcinus corrugatus* • Luaineachán rúscach

The Wrinkled Swimming Crab, which gets its name from its furrowed texture, is one of the less commonly seen swimming crabs. This one is a female and is carrying a mass of bright orange eggs – in this condition she is said to be 'berried'.

If examined in close up, the Edible Crab can be seen to have small green eyes, intricate, feather-like mouth parts and to be covered in small white spots. The carapace (as the hard outer shell is known) is marvellously detailed and this detail can even be seen on a cast off carapace, shed by the crab as it grows. In order to grow, it removes the older covering which has become too small, to reveal a new, pristine and larger carapace. In overview the Edible Crab's upper body 'shell' has edges which look remarkably like the pressed-down pastry edges of an old fashioned, handmade pie.

Edible Eater

EDIBLE CRAB
Cancer pagurus • **Portán dearg**

Here an Edible Crab is sitting amidst numerous Common Starfish, and like them, is simply waiting for a meal to drop down, literally, from above. The rocky coast of Dursey Island is fringed with mussels, which are constantly dislodged by waves. When they fall to the seabed below they provide a tasty, fresh, pre-packed meal for a multitude of waiting diners.

The crab is able to use its claws to crush the mussel shells until they crack open and it can remove the contents. Starfish open mussels more slowly (see page 55).

Designed to Swim

HARBOUR CRAB
Liocarcinus depurator • Luaineachán gormchosach

When they feel threatened Harbour Crabs will sit back, splay their legs to make themselves look larger, and raise their clawed legs upwards in a menacing posture. They appear to have no concept of size and will threaten a diver far bigger than themselves with no qualms whatsoever. They are vicious little creatures and attack often seems to be their idea of the best form of defence. This can also be a ploy though, and sometimes they will take advantage of the surprise generated by their apparent aggressiveness to swim quickly away.

A Paddler

The Harbour Crab's rearmost legs show it to be a swimming crab. These legs end in paddles rather than in the pointed claws that other crabs have. The paddles enable them to swim surprisingly effectively (sideways of course). Harbour Crabs' paddles are often purple or purple-tinged, which helps to identify them, and when displaying to each other they wave these brightly coloured 'paddles' above and behind them. The crab in the photograph is both distinctively coloured and patterned on the top of its body, but this is not always the case as these crabs can be very light in colour and often have little or no patterning at all.

The best hiding place that the Harbour Crab has is usually below it – these animals are expert burrowers and seem to simply sink into soft sand in a matter of seconds, leaving only their eyes above the surface to keep an eye on the world. This one, though, is sheltering beneath a handy piece of broken kelp, the colour and shape of which just happens to conceal it rather well.

Mostly on the Shore

SHORE CRAB
Carcinus maenas • **Portán glas**

As its name suggests, this very common crab is the one most often found on the shore – in rockpools and under stones. In suitable locations they are also found in shallow water where they can be seen digging for anything edible under the seabed. This one is on maerl, but on sandy seabeds they will dig holes as they look for food, or even bury themselves like Harbour Crabs do. They vary in colour and are sometimes known as Green Crabs, in areas where this is their predominant colour.

Sometimes on the Shore

RISSO'S CRAB • probably *Xantho pilipes* • **Portán Risso**

There are several of these small Xanthidae crabs found around Ireland and none has a common name, although in general terms they are sometimes referred to as mud, rubble or pebble crabs. This is because they usually live on 'rough ground' of mud, sand, pebbles and cobbles, often hiding under the larger stones. The one in the photograph is probably *Xantho pilipes* which has hairy walking legs.

Although not uncommon, these little crabs are rarely seen as they live near to or at extreme low water on the shore, or at slightly greater depths where only scuba divers can see them.

VELVET SWIMMING CRAB • *Necora puber* • Luaineachán

This pair of crabs is 'clasped', not mating. The top crab is the male and he is holding onto the female until she is ready to mate. He is quite prepared to defend them both, as is clearly demonstrated in this photograph, taken nearly 30 years ago!

Hermit crabs use discarded shells to provide armour for their own rather soft (and tasty) bodies. Sometimes these shells have a covering of small animals themselves, which can give the hermit crabs the appearance of having a 'fur' coating – as can be seen clearly in this close-up. The animals are small hydroids (related to anemones) and are specific to the type of hermit crab inhabiting the shell.

One House but two Inhabitants

COMMON HERMIT CRAB
Pagurus bernhardus • **Faocha ghliomaigh**

An overall picture of the Common Hermit Crab shows just how extensively its shell can be covered in hydroids. These hermit crabs can be found wandering on all sorts of seabeds as they forage. Often they will feel around with their pincers and pick things up to see if they are edible before dropping them and moving on. If disturbed and frightened, they take cover right inside their shells until nothing can be seen of them; although where suitable shells are in short supply, some crabs may use shells which are a little small and they may not fit inside quite so snugly or invisibly!

Cloak and Stinger

ANEMONE HERMIT CRAB
Pagurus prideaux • **Faocha ghliomaigh ghainimh**

This hermit crab uses a shell to live in but also has an association with the Cloak Anemone (*Adamsia carcinopados*), which attaches itself to the shell. The anemone's tentacles can be seen dangling down beneath the shell, and they probably provide the crab with protection, as they will sting potential predators. If threatened, the anemone can also throw out stinging pink threads to deter attackers.

The relationship between this particular crab and anemone is 'obligatory', as the only time that they are likely to be seen separately is when one of them has died. Just occasionally, an empty shell with the anemone on it can be found.

Sought After

CRAWFISH or SPINY LOBSTER
Palinurus elephas • **Piardóg, Gliomach spíonach coiteann**

Individual crawfish now live in rocky areas where once rows of them could be seen lining ledges. Such sights are rare these days as they are in great demand. Valued for their fine flavour, they command a high price and so are heavily fished-for.

They are orange-red and do not have large claws like their cousin the (blue) lobster. They feed on worms and small crabs and a fully-grown adult can reach over 50 cm in length and weigh several kilos. Crawfish are sometimes referred to as Crayfish or Crays, probably wrongly as crayfish are actually a freshwater creature.

Large Crawfish are ideally suited to deep ledges where their feelers have freedom to move around.

COMMON LOBSTER • *Homarus gammarus* • Gliomach

This lobster has found an ideal crevice in which to live. If such a home does not already exist, then a lobster will often construct one by digging out sand and gravel, and even small rocks, from under a suitable boulder, leaving a pile of debris sitting in front of its home as a tell-tale sign of its presence.

SQUAT LOBSTER • *Galathea squamifera* **(Galatheidae)** • **(Gliomach gogaideach)**

As its name indicates, the Squat Lobster is a much smaller relation of the Common Lobster. Most are crevice dwellers, so little can be seen of them, but they are also nocturnal and wander out into the open under the cover of darkness when they can be both seen and photographed.

DUBLIN BAY PRAWN or SCAMPI • *Nephops norvegicus* • Cloicheán bhá Bhaile Átha Cliath, Sceaimpí

These animals live in burrows excavated in seabeds which have mud of a suitable consistency. They usually live in deeper water, as little such mud generally exists close inshore, except in unusual places such as Lough Hyne in Co. Cork.

A SHRIMP • probably *Processa canaliculata* **(Caridea)** • **(Séacla)**

There are many different types of shrimp in the coastal waters surrounding Ireland. Some, like this one, are nocturnal and so are rarely seen and are difficult to identify. This colourful shrimp is a 'berried' female whose greenish-bluish eggs can clearly be seen contrasted against her redder body.

See-through Prawn

COMMON PRAWN
Palaemon serratus • Cloicheán coiteann

The bodies of many small crustaceans are almost transparent so they can be very inconspicuous. Here the camera-lighting is illuminating the prawn from behind, making its transparency and internal organs quite clearly visible. Prawns like this one often live in crevices, under boulders in shallow water and even in rockpools, but will come out to forage at night (which is when this photograph was taken).

Stealthy Hunter

BROWN SHRIMP
Crangon crangon • Séacla coiteann

Shrimps lie partially buried in sandy seabeds. They are difficult to see until they dart across the seabed and give themselves away. Their disruptive colouration and patterning are ideally suited to their stealthy method of lying low so as to capture prey as it passes. They are surprisingly vicious little creatures and are 'hunters', actively attacking prey which strays too close.

Starfish
& Relatives

Starfish vary in size and shape. Some are traditionally five-legged and about the size of a hand; others have many more arms or have thin, brittle arms which are easily lost (brittlestars), whilst others have featherlike arms (feather stars).

Starfish are able to regenerate arms if these are lost, and it is not uncommon to see starfish with one or two shorter, thinner arms where these are re-growing. Occasionally a damaged arm will re-grow as two and so a five-armed starfish may finally end up with six or even more arms.

Relatives of starfish include both sea urchins and sea cucumbers. Sometimes there are obvious signs of this relationship (for example, all have 'tube-feet'), but often it is not so obvious.

Many dead sea urchin's tests (the name given to their hard, oval, outer skeleton) have been used as curios and sold as such, but in life an urchin's test is covered in sharp spines to deter predators. Between the spines are numerous tube-feet and other small organs designed to help clean the urchin and perform other functions.

Sea cucumbers are odd creatures. The Cotton Spinner moves so slowly across the seabed that for most of the time it appears just to lie there, although it is probably casually munching away at any edible material on the rocks on which it is found. Other cucumbers are crevice- or sand/mud-dwellers and all that can be seen of these creatures is the fine spray of extended tentacles that they use to trap particles of food drifting by.

COMMON STARFISH
Asterias rubens • Crosóg mhara choiteann

Common Starfish can be found in rockpools, washed up on the strandline or on the seabed. They can be very abundant creatures and when conditions are suitable, can be found in vast numbers.

Holding On

COMMON STARFISH
Asterias rubens • Crosóg mhara choiteann

Common Starfish are found on many seabeds. Here, a starfish is clambering along a kelp frond and using its tube feet to secure a tight grip as the kelp is 'blown' about by the current. Large numbers of Common Starfish are sometimes found washed up on the strandline after storms. Many live in relatively shallow water, where sudden bad weather can catch them out and wash them up.

Fast Mover

SAND STAR
Astropecten irregularis • Crosóg ghainimh

As its name suggests, this starfish lives on sandy seabeds. Often they are found partially buried, but when they want to move they can do so surprisingly quickly. Some, like the one shown here, are quite colourful – nearly orange and with purple leg ends – but many are far more drab and are perfectly camouflaged by the sand in which they live.

SPINY STARFISH • *Marthasterias glacialis* • Crosóg choilgneach

Mussels are a favoured food of starfish. In order to eat a mussel, a starfish will grip the two shells and will attempt to prise them apart. It will exert a strong force for such a long time that the mussel's muscles eventually tire. Once the shells open, the starfish is able to eat the contents.

CUSHION STAR • *Asterina gibbosa* • Crosóg fhaoilinne

Cushion Stars are appropriately named, as they are short-legged, relatively stout and really quite cushion-like! Most are rather small, measuring only 2~3 cm across their arms, but there are a few larger ones to be found in Irish waters.

BLOODY HENRY STARFISH • *Henricia* **sp.** • Crosóg Anraí

Although some of these starfish really are blood-red in colour, their colouring can actually be quite variable, and ranges from yellows through oranges to reds and purple as shown here. These starfish also have a distinctive stiff, sandpapery texture.

Fragile Arms

SAND BRITTLESTAR
Ophiura ophiura • Crosóg bhriosc ghainimh

Concealment is a defensive strategy adopted by many marine animals that live on sand and can bury themselves in it. Sand Brittlestars are one of the animals that do this. Upon sensing food, they clamber out of the sand and sidle over to it with considerable speed. Conversely, they burrow into the sand when they sense danger.

Feather Blanket

FEATHER STAR
Antedon bifida • Cleiteach mhara

Feather Stars can be found singly or densely packed in vast numbers that entirely cover the seabed. They use their arms, which really do resemble feathers, to filter edible morsels from the passing water. They then transfer this food down these feather-like arms to their central mouth.

In this photograph, Feather Stars are sitting on the seabed alongside large numbers of Common Brittlestars. Both are filter feeding in an area which is rich in water-borne edible material. Between them they cover virtually the entire seabed when conditions permit them to do so.

COMMON BRITTLESTAR • *Ophiothrix fragilis* • Crosóg bhriosc choiteann

As might be expected, these delicate starfish have fragile arms, which can be very easily lost but fortunately do regenerate. Like Feather Stars, brittlestars can be found in vast numbers, covering large areas of suitable seabed.

GREEN SHORE URCHIN • *Psammechinus miliaris* • Cuán mara glas

The Green Shore Urchin is usually a mix of green and purple in colour and is one of the smaller urchins found in Irish waters. It normally grows to about 5 cm in diameter.

Feet but No Legs

EDIBLE SEA URCHIN
Echinus esculentus • **Cuán mara coiteann**

A close look at sea urchins shows that they have numerous small, flexible tubes growing between their spines. These are called tube-feet and allow the animal to move around by utilising hydraulic suction. Small pincers also grow between the spines and help the animal to keep itself clean. Sometimes small balls of rolled up detritus can be seen on the seabed below an urchin; these are made up of material which has been removed from the urchin by the pincers.

A Family Resemblance

SEVEN-ARMED STARFISH
Luidia ciliaris • **Crosóg na seacht méar**

Starfish and urchins are closely related, as can be seen from this photograph. This starfish, like many others, has a rigid body and so moves around on tube-feet which are quite effective and which enable it to move rapidly.

Cucumber Garnish

A BURROWING SEA CUCUMBER
Thyone fusus • Súmaire cladaigh uachasach

Some sea cucumbers live buried in gravel, soft sand and even in mud. As such seabeds often stir up easily, these creatures can be difficult to see and photograph in what is all too frequently murky water.

When feeding, they extend their tentacles into the water to catch edible material as it drifts past. They then slowly bring the tentacles to their mouth (situated at the base of the tentacles) in order to eat what they have caught. This feeding process takes place so gradually that it appears to be in slow motion.

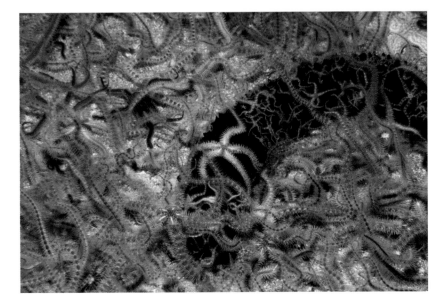

Diverse but Related

This Cotton Spinner sea cucumber is lying on the seabed amidst a 'bed' of Common Brittlestars, along with a Common Starfish at the top right of the picture. All these creatures are echinoderms and so are related, despite appearing to be quite different from each other. Whilst the Cotton Spinner is a very slow-moving animal and the Common Starfish not much faster, the brittlestars can often be seen writhing around and making the whole seabed seem to be a mass of movement.

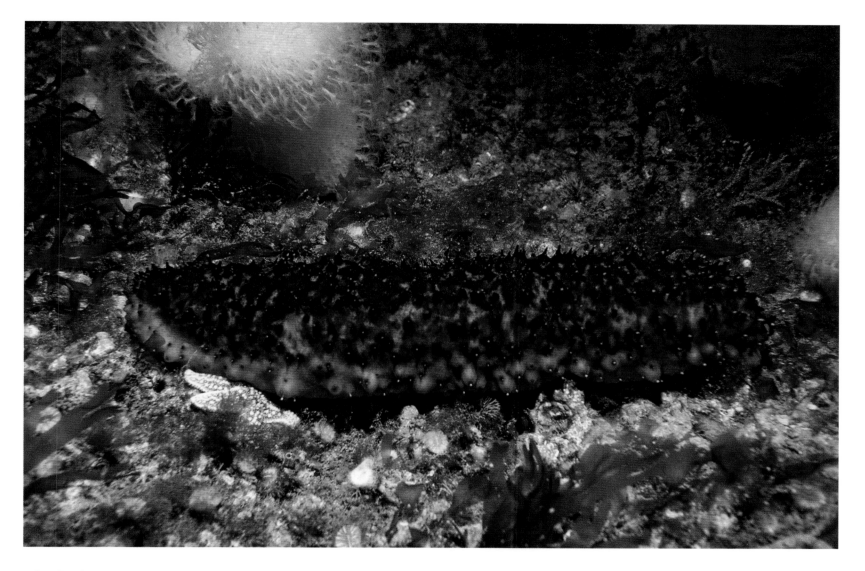

COTTON SPINNER or BLACK SEA CUCUMBER • *Holothuria forskali* • **Súmaire cladaigh dubh**

If the Cotton Spinner is stressed, it can eject white threads – hence its name. These threads are the toxic Cuvierian organ. It is probably not a good idea to handle this animal as people have been known to develop sensitivity to such holothurians.

Fish

Although fish may be the most familiar of marine animals, few people actually know a great deal about them. Many fish live along the Irish coast or visit Irish waters and they vary greatly in both colour and shape.

In fact, it is difficult to say just how many species of fish have been found around the Irish coast because some are very rarely seen, perhaps because they have wandered inshore from deeper water or may have arrived from other countries in the ballast water of ships. A good estimate is something between 400~500 different species, ranging from the smallest, which is less than 2 cm long when fully grown, to fish that are several metres in length.

Fish have many shapes, adaptations and modifications. Many flatfish actually lie on one side, whilst others like the Angler Fish have a flattened body but are actually still upright. The Angler is adapted so that it when it lies still it blends in with the seabed, and it has an intriguing modification – its 'lure', which it waves around in order to attract smaller fish close to its enormous mouth. The Scaldfish has truly amazing and highly effective colouration and patterning, so suited to the seabed it is found on that it is almost impossible to spot.

Although our ideas about fish tend to be limited by the silvery or sometimes drab commercial species seen in shops, many Irish fish are highly colourful. Wrasse in particular would not seem out of place swimming over a tropical coral reef.

CUCKOO WRASSE
Labrus mixtus • Ballach Muire

Male Cuckoo Wrasse are both inquisitive and territorially aggressive. They will often peer into an underwater camera lens and have been known to repeatedly bite at a diver and even draw blood if they can find any exposed flesh!

These brightly-coloured small fish are Rock Cook and they like areas covered in kelp or seaweed. They swim in small numbers – hardly shoals – and are always ready to dart for cover if they feel threatened. However, their curiosity often seems to get the better of them and groups of these fish will often follow divers around.

Flashes of Colour

ROCK COOK
Centrolabrus exoletus • Ballach fuarleice

This close-up reveals just how colourful a Rock Cook really is. They are a timid fish and are often only glimpsed underwater, where they tend to stay at a distance from visiting divers. This makes it hard to see their brilliant colours, so their real beauty is only revealed when photographs capture them properly. Whilst not uncommon, their reluctance to swim close to divers and their small size make them the least-known member of the wrasse family.

Most Colourful

CUCKOO WRASSE
Labrus mixtus • Ballach Muire

The male Cuckoo Wrasse, in his vivid orange and blue mix of distinctive breeding-colours, is probably the most colourful fish in the seas around Ireland. He is a most striking and handsome fish, but actually started life as a female before changing and becoming a dominant male, surrounded by other drabber-looking females. Dominant males are protective of their females and can be very aggressive indeed. They also exhibit a mixture of curiosity and caution and will swim slowly up to a diver to get a good look before suddenly darting into a nearby crevice.

Young wrasse can be difficult to differentiate. This one is a smallish fish and is probably a young Ballan or a Goldsinny Wrasse. It has found a useful shelf (or should that be hand?) of Dead Men's Fingers on which to snooze, on an otherwise near-vertical rocky wall off Connemara, on the west coast of Ireland.

Cheeky Chappie

GOLDSINNY WRASSE
Ctenolabrus rupestris • Bod gorm

This small wrasse can be distinguished from other wrasse by the black spot on its back, just in front of its tail. Although small, it is often quite a daring little fish. It is known to remove parasites from the bodies of larger fish, helping to clean them. In return it may be left in peace and so be unafraid of many larger creatures. Here it can be seen swimming above a spiny starfish in Lough Hyne, Co. Cork.

Reef Fish

BALLAN WRASSE
Labrus bergylta • Ballach breac

The largest of the wrasses is the Ballan Wrasse. It is a deep-bodied solid fish and is common in areas of rock and kelp. It feeds on various hard-shelled creatures and in order to be able to do so it uses special grinding structures in its throat called the pharyngeal bones, which look like a set of very rounded teeth. The fish in the photograph is a large, sturdy and distinctly patterned animal and is swimming over bedrock reefs off Kilkee, Co. Clare.

Unusual or Merely Seldom Seen?

BAILLON'S WRASSE
Crenilabrus bailloni • **Ballach Baillon**

Whilst there are few records of Baillon's Wrasse from around the coasts of Ireland, there are a limited number of records of these fish from the Connemara area. As these are spread over many years, this suggests that a population of these wrasse may have been living there for quite some time. They are usually found much further south, around France, although there are some records from the south English coast, from the North Sea and more recently from South Wales.

One of the problems in identifying this fish is that it can look very similar to the far more common Corkwing Wrasse, with which it is easily confused. As Baillon's Wrasse is much less familiar to most people than the Corkwing Wrasse, it may well be seen but mis-identified.

Baillon's wrasse like seagrass beds with rock nearby.

The top photo shows a male Baillon's Wrasse looking into the nest (a tube-like structure) that he has built on a rocky reef from pieces of seaweed. A female will lay eggs inside the nest for the male to guard.

The lower photo shows one of these fish asleep on the seabed amidst seagrass. When the water is cold this wrasse can easily be found asleep (but with open eyes) on the seabed. This may be because Baillon's Wrasse are usually found in warmer water and sleeping is a good way to conserve precious energy in the cooler months.

RED or PORTUGUESE BLENNY • *Parablennius ruber* • Ceannruán rua, Ceannruán Portaingéalach

For a long time the Red or Portuguese Blenny was confused with the Tompot Blenny. This photograph shows a male fish in breeding colours. The picture was originally published in "Sherkin Comment" in 2003, and as a result, the species was noted in the Journal of Fish Biology. Since then many sightings have been recorded around Ireland's west coast.

Poor Swimmer

GREATER PIPEFISH
Syngnathus acus • **Snáthaid mhara mhór**

Pipefish are close relatives of the seahorse. In many ways they do resemble a straightened-out seahorse, especially as they have a similarly-shaped snout. They are not strong swimmers and are usually seen simply swaying with the current as they wait for small edible morsels to drift past. Studies have shown that some pipefish will then make a sudden, extremely high-speed snap at the morsel – which quite simply vanishes into the pipefish's mouth.

It is the male pipefish which actually carries the eggs, laid by the female, until they hatch.

Slippery Customer

BUTTERFISH or GUNNEL
Pholis gunnellus • **Sleamhnóg airgid**

This fish can be found in rockpools on the shore, as well as in shallow and deeper water. The Butterfish's name is believed to come from the fact that it has a covering of a very slimy mucus, which means that if it is caught in the hands it can slip through fingers like butter! A long eel-like little fish, it is prettily and characteristically marked, but sadly it always appears to wear a look of extreme misery with its large baleful eyes and distinctly down-turned mouth!

RETICULATED DRAGONET • *Callionymus reticulatus* • Iascán líontánach

There are three different Dragonets found around Ireland. Of these, the males can be easy to differentiate between but not the females and juveniles. Despite being common and frequently seen by scuba divers, they are not seen very often by anglers or rockpoolers.

Family Fish

SHANNY or BLENNY
Blennius pholis • Ceannruán

Small Shannies are a very common rockpool fish but they can be very small; indeed, when in rockpools they may only be a centimetre or so long. Bigger, older fish can reach as much as 30 cm in length and prefer crevices in shallow water. Dark-coloured males like this one, which was found in the old stone jetty in Lough Hyne, Co. Cork, are usually breeding fish and may well be guarding eggs laid by a female in a suitable crevice.

Shannies are one of several fish that can actually survive out of water for several hours. If left stranded by a receding tide they will stay damp under a stone or seaweed until the water returns.

Always Curious

TOMPOT BLENNY
Parablennius gattorugine • Ceannruán rocach

Tompots are very inquisitive members of the blenny family and simply cannot resist having a look at what is going on. They will often peer out from under rocks or from inside crevices and will even swim out if they want to see more. Their curiosity allows them to be photographed easily and this, together with their appealing face and guileless expressions, has made them one of the best known of the blennies. Their pictures have even appeared on book covers such as "Ireland's Marine Life".

BUTTERFLY BLENNY • *Blennius ocellaris* • Ceannruán féileacáin

Male Butterfly Blennies will guard eggs laid by the female, often in an old whelk shell. They are excellent fathers and can be seen gently blowing water over their eggs to keep them in perfect condition. They will not leave the eggs and have been found in shells trawled up and emptied onto the decks of fishing boats.

Scaly Head

ROCK GOBY
Gobius paganellus • Mac siobháin carraige

These small, solitary fish can be found both in shallow water and in rockpools. Here, one is sitting under some seaweed, in only a few metres of water, while it surveys the scene.

Breeding males often have a light tip to their dorsal fins, which can vary from cream to bright orange in colour. In colder weather they have been found down to a depth of about 20 m.

Rock Gobies are similar to Black Gobies in size and shape and can be similar in colour. Unlike the Black Goby, they have scales on top of their head and this helps differentiate them.

Seldom Seen, Always Spotted

LEOPARD-SPOTTED GOBY
Thorogobius ephippiatus • Mac siobháin ballach

This fish was virtually unknown from around the Irish coast until scuba diving grew in popularity. It is very rarely seen due to the inaccessible places in which it lives, and it is still usually seen only by divers. These gobies like overhung bedrock crevices and will lie at the entrance watching everything around them, ready to dart back into the safety of their narrow home at any hint of danger. Some fish have light coloured fin tips, which may signify that they are breeding males as it does in some other gobies like the rock goby.

FRIES'S GOBY • *Lesueurigobius friesii* • Mac siobháin Fries

This handsome fish lives in burrows in suitable muddy seabeds. Despite its dull surroundings, it is a striking fish with brown blotches on a sometimes purplish body, and often has distinct yellow markings too. They frequently sit with their heads just poking out from their burrows.

Lough Hyne, Ireland's only Marine Nature Reserve, is in a beautiful setting, nestled amongst the hills of West Cork. All the marine life within its waters is protected by law, and it boasts some rare and highly unusual inhabitants.

The Gobies in Lough Hyne

RED-MOUTHED GOBY
Gobius cruentatus • **Mac siobháin deargbhéalach**

Red-mouthed Gobies are normally found in the Mediterranean but their distribution extends as far north as Ireland, where they are occasionally recorded. These colourful fish are now known from a few places around the Irish coast. There are some in the sea by the Kenmare River, Co. Kerry, and marine biologists have studied them in Lough Hyne, Co. Cork. They are large but relatively shy gobies and usually retreat into crevices and under boulders when approached.

COUCH'S GOBY
Gobius couchi • **Mac siobháin Couch**

This rather nondescript-looking goby was identified as a separate species only as recently as 1974. It is notoriously difficult to differentiate from the very similar-looking Black Goby, but for those interested in gobies, there are different characteristics that can be observed. In Lough Hyne, where Couch's and Black Gobies can be seen together, it is easier to compare them and their subtle differences are more obvious.

CONGER EEL • *Conger conger* • **Eascann choncair**

Although Conger Eels have a fearsome reputation, this is probably largely undeserved as even big (2 m long) fish have relatively small teeth. Congers love crevices or suitable holes under boulders or amongst wreckage. It appears that they sit still for long periods of time, as they are often covered in a dusting of silt.

Crevice Dwellers

BLACK GOBY
Gobius niger • Mac siobháin dubh

Black Gobies are another fish which likes crevices, or any hole into which they can retreat for protection. Despite their desire for a handy refuge, they are curious. Although they will disappear into their hidey-hole if disturbed, they will soon pop their heads out again as they inevitably want to find out what is going on.

Gobies have rows of sensory receptors on their faces but these are not usually visible on most species. On the Black Goby they can be seen as lines of fine toothcomb-like rows below the eyes (see photograph on the right).

Although called Black Gobies, these fish are very variable in colour, displaying shades from a mottled fawn to much darker colours, including blue – as in this old male above.

PLAICE • *Pleuronectes platessa* • **Leathóg bhallach**

Flatfish actually lie on one of their sides. If you look carefully at a flatfish's face, you can see that one of the eyes has moved around to its current position from the side that the fish is now lying on, but its mouth is still located between both sides.

To hide itself, a fish like the Plaice will settle onto a sandy seabed and then wriggle into the sediment, scattering sand over its fins. This breaks up its outline and, together with the blotchy pattern on the uppermost side of the fish, makes it difficult to spot. Plaice often have distinct orange spots on their upperside, as do some Flounders, although those of the latter are not usually so obvious.

Thorny Wings

A close look at the eye of a Thornback Ray reveals it to be intricately patterned. Below the eye is the spiracle, a part of its breathing system although the mouth itself lies on the underside of the fish. If one looks carefully, it is possible to see some of the thorns that are scattered over the Thornback Ray's head and back and which are responsible for its common name.

Mermaid's Purse

The eggcases produced by rays and skates are known as Mermaid's Purses and the one shown here is from a Thornback Ray. Each ray and skate produces its own char-acteristically-sized and shaped eggcase. The embryonic ray inside develops over many months, whilst protected by the tough outer casing. The case is built so that the ray inside can get a fresh supply of oxygenated water by moving around and creating a slight current to draw fresh seawater in through small apertures in the 'horns'. Little is known about where these eggcases are laid and it is extremely rare to find one underwater with a live embryo inside it.

THORNBACK RAY • *Raja clavata* • Roc garbh

Thornback Rays often lie motionless on a flat, sandy seabed with a scattering of sediment over them, which helps to break up their outline. When they swim off, their characteristic shape becomes clear. These fish swim with a gentle motion due to the graceful and smooth beating of their 'wings'.

Blending In

THOR'S SCALDFISH
Arnoglossus thori • Scoilteán Túir

Scaldfish are a rarely-seen flatfish. Their patterning and colouration may help explain why, because they blend in almost perfectly with the seabed, especially in the dull, low-contrast conditions found underwater. This one is Thor's Scaldfish and though it is found in relatively shallow water, it is still an unusual sighting. When netted, the Scaldfish tends to shed its scales, which gives it a 'scalded' look, and its name.

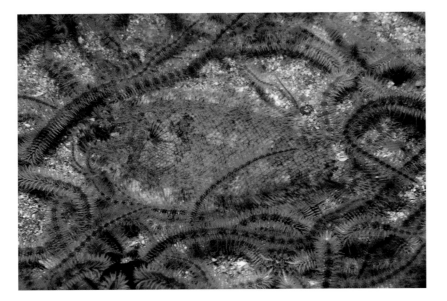

Colour Shifter

NORWEGIAN TOPKNOT
Phrynorhombus norvegicus • Leathóg leice Ioruach

There are three topknots found in the seas around Ireland. This one, the Norwegian Topknot, is a small flatfish, which only grows to about 12 cm in length. It has large, distinctive scales and is able to change its body-colour in order to blend in with its current surroundings. Here one is sitting on bedrock, which has pink encrusting algae on it and a scattering of sand. There are brittlestars on the rock as well and the topknot has altered its colours to blend in pretty effectively.

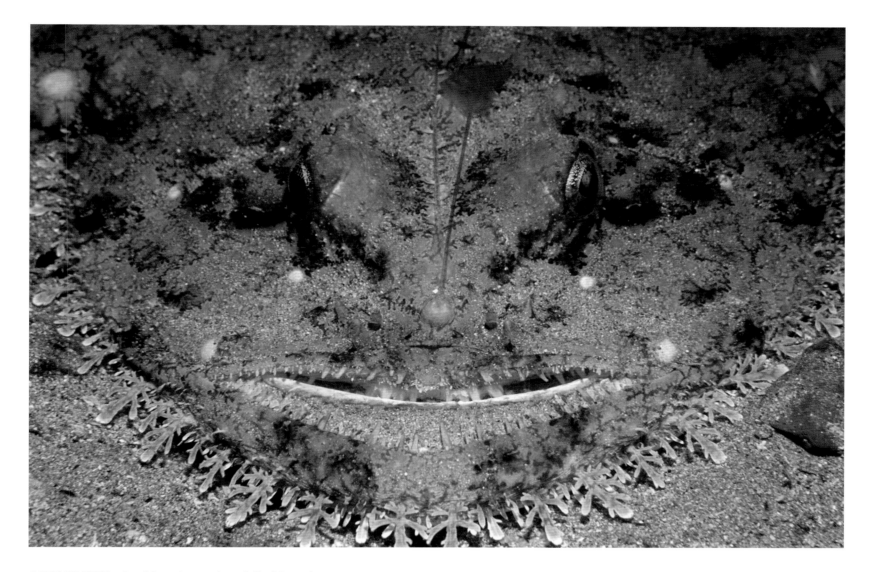

ANGLER FISH • *Lophius piscatorius* • **Láimhíneach**

The Angler sits and waits. It has a lure above its mouth, which it waves around to attract the attention of its dinner, relying on camouflage to conceal its true identity. When something edible is within range it is snapped up into the fish's huge mouth and gulped down.

Shellfish

Most shellfish, as their name suggests, are creatures with a shell or shells, although not all shellfish have shells and not all marine creatures with a hard outer covering or 'shell' are actually shellfish. There are many types of shellfish. Some, such as the humble Periwinkle, rely entirely on their shells for protection; others hide, in addition to having shells. (Razor Shells bury themselves in sand and use a siphon to breathe, and whilst Scallops do partially bury themselves, they can also swim away from danger if they really have to). Others rely on different methods of protection, for example by tasting awful or by collecting stinging cells from anemones, which they then use themselves.

One of the best-known of all shellfish is the Common or Blue Mussel which coats many hard surfaces between and below the tides. It is cultivated in Ireland and is an important part of the aquaculture industry. Mussels have two shells, which are held open or shut by a very strong muscle. When covered by water, the animal opens it shells and pumps seawater through its body to extract both oxygen and food. The shell protects the tasty mussel from being eaten, with varying degrees of success.

Shells come in many shapes and sizes, some textured like the Cowrie's, others rough, sharp and haphazard in shape like that of the oyster. Perhaps surprisingly, some relations of shellfish have either an internal shell or as in the case of sea slugs, no shell at all.

One of the most numerous hard 'shelled' creatures found on hard, rocky surfaces is the barnacle. The barnacle is actually a relative of the crab and should not really be included in this section at all.

ROUGH PERIWINKLE
Littorina saxatilis • **Faocha gharbh**

Rough Periwinkles live high up on the shore where they are often found in cracks and fissures. They can measure up to 18 mm in size but most are much smaller. As can be seen from the photograph, in some places there can be almost too many for the available living space.

MUSSEL • *Mytilus edulis* • Diúilicín

Mussels often live on rocky coasts and can be found well above the low tide mark where they are subjected to battering from waves. They use their 'beard' (byssus threads) to anchor themselves to the rock but even so, many do not survive and are broken open by the sea or by predators.

Life in the Extreme

MUSSEL • *Mytilus edulis* • Diúilicín

LIMPET • *Patella* sp. • Bairneach

Rocky shores are where rockpools are found. These pools are home to creatures that are adapted to surviving in the extremely variable conditions found in them.

At high tide, when the water covers the shore, rockpools become another part of the undersea world, and are subjected to currents, wave action and the cooler temperatures of water washed in from the open sea.

At low tide the pools are still and calm and in hot summer weather they can heat up quickly from the sun.

Rockpools provide an insight into the undersea world because they provide an opportunity to see plants and animals on the seashore that can normally only survive and be seen in permanently-submerged areas.

When covered by the seawater, mussels will open their shells in order to feed.

SPOTTED or EUROPEAN COWRIE • *Trivia monacha* • Fínicín Eorpach

Cowries are found worldwide but those from Ireland are far smaller that their tropical relatives, reaching only a little over 1 cm in length. This one is climbing over some translucent red seaweed, on the underside of which is a juvenile Common Starfish.

PAINTED TOPSHELL • *Calliostoma zizyphinum* • Faochán Muire dathannach

This topshell is often brightly patterned and is distinctly pointed. It is found on rocky shores and seabeds and in this photograph is resting on some Boring Sponge. On its back is a passenger – a barnacle which can be seen filter-feeding.

BARNACLES and WORMS

Although they are not shellfish, the barnacles and tube worms in this photograph both have a hard outer covering. When they die, this hard shell-like outer covering is broken up by the pounding waves and eventually helps form the sand so familiar on beaches.

On the Shore

COMMON PERIWINKLE
Littorina littorea • **Gioradán, Faocha**

Periwinkles primarily graze on algae and like fairly sheltered seaweed-rich shores, on which they can be extremely abundant. Many can be seen in rockpools and on rocks and boulders when the tide is out. They are edible and archaeologists have even found their shells in ancient middens (human domestic-waste material), indicating that they have been eaten for nearly 10,000 years.

Returning Home

LIMPET
***Patella* sp.** • **Bairneach**

Most Limpets are shore-dwellers, and have strong, thick, heavy shells, which are needed to withstand battering wave action and to discourage predators. Individual limpets have a spot on the rock to which they return after a feeding foray. Limpets can be very abundant on some shores and can live for many years.

Two Shells

RAZOR SHELL
Ensis sp. • Scian mhara

Razor Shells are burrowing bivalves, and use a siphon pushed up through the surface of the sand in which they live, to pump water down to them, enabling them to both breathe and feed. At any sign of danger (they are very sensitive to nearby disturbance) they can retract their siphon and rapidly descend into their burrow. Several different Razor Shells are found in Irish waters, but with only a small section of the animal's shell showing in the photograph it is difficult to identify which one this is.

Bivalve Siphon

Each type of burrowing bivalve has a different siphon but it is difficult to identify them from their siphons alone. Siphons have an inhalant and exhalant section, both of which are clearly visible in this particularly colourful picture of one. Siphons vary in length depending on how deep under the sediment their owners live.

COMMON or FLAT OYSTER • *Ostrea edulis* • Oisre leathan

Oysters were once regarded as a poor man's food. That was when they were extremely abundant but they have become scarce and are now considered to be a delicacy. Most oysters eaten in Ireland today are actually Pacific Oysters, which are successfully farmed here.

Wary Watchers

Surprisingly scallops can actually swim! They do so by opening and closing their two shells rapidly and creating a gush of water, which is expelled in the opposite direction from that in which they then travel. This is an ungainly method of swimming and is only used in an emergency. Scallops will swim when they detect a potential predator and feel threatened, such as when a hungry starfish touches them. As a starfish will eat a scallop if it can get a good grip and prise the shells apart, the ability to be able to swim off before one can gain a hold is very useful.

Free or Attached

VARIEGATED SCALLOP
Chlamys varia • **Cluaisín garbh**

There are several different species of scallop found in Irish waters. The best known are the edible "Kings" and "Queenies". This Variegated Scallop is also quite a common species and can either attach itself to a firm base (as shown here, where two are attached to an empty oyster shell), or be free-living. Unlike the larger varieties, which are fished for, Variegated Scallops are too small (measuring up to 6 cm) to be of any commercial value.

QUEEN SCALLOP or "QUEENIE" • *Aequipecten opercularis* • **Cluaisín**

Queen Scallops are usually partially buried in the seabed in which they live. If a scallop has been disturbed and has swum away from danger it can be found lying out in the open, on top of the seabed. Their blue 'eyes' can detect changes in light – and so possible danger.

Textured Sea Slug

Cadlina laevis (Nudibranchia) • (Bodalach)

Sea slugs challenge most people's perception of slugs. The extraordinary beauty and colour of these maritime cousins of the garden slug make them one of the underwater photographer's favourite subjects. Sea slugs come in a great variety of shapes and sizes. Although most are quite small – just a few centimetres at most – others can be substantial animals and grow up to 20 cm long. Whilst some are brightly coloured, others, like this one, have subdued colours but detailed textures. This sea slug feeds on sponges as do many others.

Cool Customer

Onchidoris muricata (Nudibranchia) • (Bodalach)

This handsome sea slug eats encrusting bryozoans, such as the Sea Mat (*Membranipora membranacea*), which apparently grows quickly in response to being eaten by sea slugs. This species of slug varies in colour from white to yellow and is generally found on the shore or in shallow water. It is found throughout the cool waters of the northern hemisphere. It is an annual animal, and is cold-adapted, breeding earlier in more northerly areas.

Flabellina pedata (**Nudibranchia**) • (**Bodalach**)

The majority of sea slugs do not have a common name because most, like this one, are seen by too few people to have acquired one. This sea slug eats hydroids (relatives of anemones), although the one seen here is merely clambering over some Serpulid Worms.

LESSER or CURLED OCTOPUS • *Eledone cirrhosa* • Ochtapas beag

The Lesser Octopus is the species normally found in the waters around Ireland. When frightened it can change colour by expanding its pigment cells, quickly switching from a creamy white to a dark, reddish brown.

LITTLE CUTTLEFISH • **probably** *Sepiola* **sp.** • **Cudal beag**

Little Cuttlefish are small animals only a few centimetres long. They are difficult to see in the low-light conditions common under water. Sometimes they give their presence away by ejecting puffs of ink in order to confuse potential predators. This activity can actually alert scuba divers to their presence.

Sponges, Squirts
& Other Animals

When presenting marine species in books, an accepted (scientific) order is usually followed. More explanatory text would have been required if this order had been followed here. So this chapter actually contains a miscellany of creatures brought together because they are often found in large numbers – either as aggregations or in colonies.

Sponges are in fact colonies of very small animals and are abundant around the Irish coast; not the bath sponge – this creature lives in the Mediterranean – but Ireland does have a substantial number of other colourful varieties. Some form colonies that are massive and very obvious. Others produce thin crusts over rock surfaces, and between these two extremes are numerous strangely-shaped, seemingly unrelated forms. A few creatures, such as some crabs and scallops, can also benefit by co-existing with sponges.

Sea Squirts can occur both as individuals (which can often be present in huge numbers) and in colonies. They vary dramatically in size from just a few millimetres in length to tens of centimetres. Whilst some like silty conditions, others are more at home in so-called 'surge' gullies, where they are exposed to strong forces. Many are transparent or translucent, making it possible to see their internal structures.

Other creatures, too, can be found in large numbers. The Oaten-pipe Hydroid is one of these. Luxuriant growths of these small animals appear in their full glory early in the year when the water is still cool. These hydroids may be just a few centimetres in height but can be found covering many hard seabeds in their millions.

BORING SPONGE
Cliona celata • Spúinse ceilte

This sponge's name refers to the fact that it is able to bore into old shells and rocks containing lime, rather than to any inability to interest us! It often occurs in the massive form seen here.

Penniless

PURSE SPONGE
Sycon ciliatum • **Spúinse sparáin**

Purse sponges can be found fastened onto rock, seaweed or any other reasonably solid surface. Mostly they are only a few centimetres long and of a nondescript beige colour, making them inconspicuous. However, a careful search often shows that they are present in quite large numbers, in the right conditions.

Spiky

YELLOW HEDGEHOG SPONGE
Polymastia boletiformis • **Spúinse gráinneoige buí**

There are several *Polymastia* sponges found in Irish waters and these can be very difficult to tell apart. Some are very rare and so far have only been found in Lough Hyne, near Baltimore, in Co. Cork. All have a basically similar shape, with numerous protuberances from a single central 'lump', and often only a sponge expert can distinguish between them.

AN ENCRUSTING SPONGE • *Eurypon major* (Porifera) • (Spúinse)

A small Painted Goby can be seen here, 'sitting' on a near-vertical crust of brilliant but translucent red sponge on one of the rocky walls of Lough Hyne, Co. Cork. This colourful sponge is probably *Eurypon major*, which is quite common on undersea cliff walls in the Lough.

Encruster

CRATER SPONGE
Hemimycale columella • Spúinse cráitéir

Many sponges form thinnish 'crusts' over the rock on which they are found. Crater Sponge is one of these and is one of the more easily-identified encrusting sponges. This is because around each of its fairly obvious 'craters' is a lighter rim, which is characteristic.

Translucent Fingers

CHIMNEY SPONGE
Polymastia penicillus • Spúinse scuaibe

Many sponges occur in strange forms. This one has actually formed a layer on the rock, much of which is covered in sediment; vertical 'shoots', which protrude from the sponge, are all that are clearly visible.

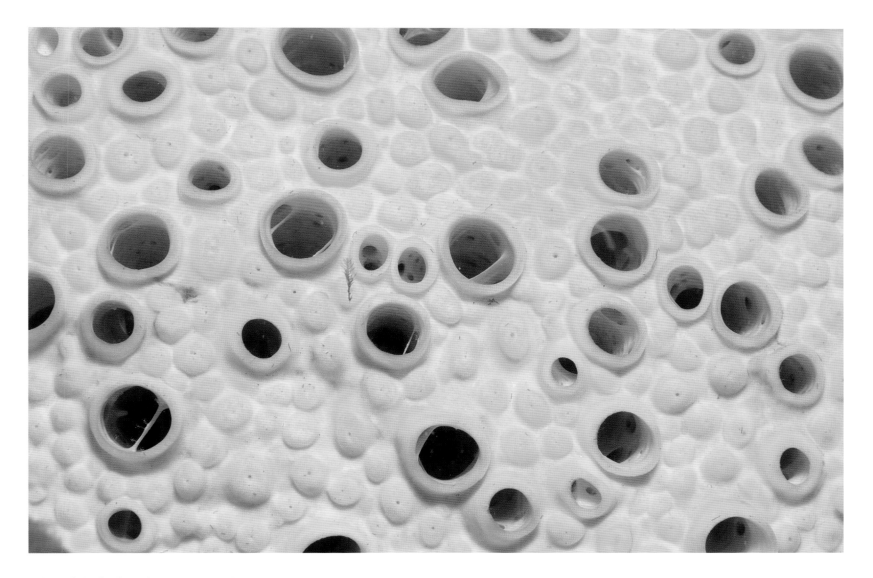

BORING SPONGE • *Cliona celata* • **Spúinse ceilte**

When viewed close-up, the massive form of the Boring Sponge shows lipped holes and short, flat protuberances. It is a firm and quite solid (rubbery) sponge, colonies of which can grow to more than 0.5 m in size.

Hitch-hiking Sponge

A HERMIT CRAB WITH A SPONGE COVERED SHELL
prob. *Suberites pagurorum*

One of the sponges found in the waters around Ireland is the Sea Orange (*Suberites ficus*). A very closely-related sponge is seen living on the hermit crab's shell in this photograph. Some *Suberites* sponges contain a marine neurotoxin protein, which is poisonous to fish, and so they probably offer the hermit crab protection. Sponges cannot generally live on softer seabeds, but when they cover a hermit crab's shell they have their own personal transport and so are able to travel around.

Soft Covering

A QUEEN SCALLOP ('QUEENIE') COVERED IN SPONGE
prob. *Suberites lutea*

'Queenies' use strong byssus threads to attach themselves to rocky seabeds for part of their lives, just as this one has done. Secured here in a crevice in a rocky seabed, it is comparatively safe. In some places, "Queenie" are fished for, so it can be prudent for them to be out of the way!

They have what is thought to be a protective and mutualistic relationship with sponges (this yellow one is thought to be *Suberites lutea*), which often cover their shells. It is thought that the sponge may protect the scallop from being eaten by starfish, whilst the presence of the scallop may help protect the sponge against attack from the Sea Lemon sea slug.

Fastening pieces of sponge all over itself provides camouflage and breaks up the outline of this small Scorpion Spider Crab. The sponge may also help to protect the crab, which is eaten by some fish, and a covering of sponge may make it unpalatable or even toxic. Eventually the sponge, which lives and clearly grows when on the crab, must become unwieldy (also see page 36).

Squirt City

A SOLITARY SEA SQUIRT
***Ascidia virginea* (Ascidiidae)** • **(Ascaid aonaránach)**

Sea squirts can be very abundant when conditions suit them. They like areas that have some water movement (which they rely on to transport food to them), but not so strong that it might dislodge them. This Sea Squirt likes somewhat sheltered, silty conditions and, whilst solitary, can also be found in large groups coating underwater rock. This is usually in places where the current is strong enough to carry silt but sometimes weak enough to deposit it also.

Many sea squirts have translucent, and sometimes even transparent, bodies.

GOOSEBERRY or BAKED-BEAN SEA SQUIRT • *Dendrodoa grossularia* • Ascaid spíonáin

These sea squirts are often found in large numbers in areas of strong water movement, including shallow surge gullies (a very difficult environment in which to live). They are frequently found together with encrusting sponges, as in this photograph.

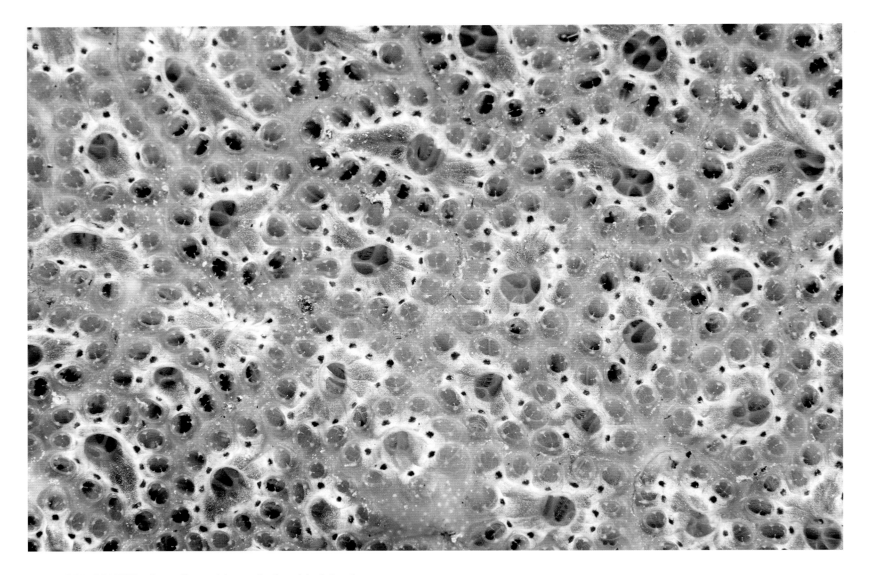

STAR SEA SQUIRT • *Botryllus schlosseri* • Ascaid réaltach

In close up, the complexity of these small colonial sea squirts can be fully appreciated. Whilst the surface is fascinating enough, a close look reveals that, inside, it has an equally complex internal structure.

Each star shape seen in this colony of Star Sea Squirts is formed from several individuals, which have congregated together around a common exhalent opening, through which the colony's waste is pumped out. A whole colony can be made up of many of these 'stars'. These squirts are on rock, which is covered in contrastingly-coloured calcareous algae and red seaweed.

LIGHT-BULB SEA SQUIRT • *Clavelina lepadiformis* • Ascaid bhairniúil

The bright, 'glowing filament-like' structures visible through the transparent bodies of these sea squirts have given rise to their common name. They are often found in 'clumps' and are eaten by the Candy-stripe Flatworm (see page 127).

Food for Others

OATEN PIPE HYDROID or TALL TUBULARIA
Tubularia indivisa • Feadánach ard

These are small animals that are related to jellyfish and sea anemones. They are included here because they can be found in vast numbers, coating all available firm surfaces, especially in the spring.

They are at their very best during early spring and, when in 'fruiting condition', have rounded pinkish reproductive bodies surrounding the mouth at the top of their stem. As the year progresses they are munched by sea slugs, which graze on them, and only the stem may remain. Here they are shown off the Skellig Islands (off the Co. Kerry coast) covering the rock below the kelp.

Many marine creatures are highly opportunistic. Here hydroids are living on the netting of a salmon farm.

Worms
& Relatives

The word worm usually conjures up images of a long, thin, wriggly animal because most of us associate it with the humble earthworm. Many marine worms are long, thin animals but in most cases the body is hidden, either buried in the seabed or contained within a tube built by the worm.

What we usually see is the far prettier part of the worm which protrudes from the seabed or out of its tube, and this is often a fan of some description, designed to catch small edible particles as they pass. These fans can be large, graceful affairs with a degree of iridescence about them, or highly-coloured stubby fans. Others are delicate sprays of thin, featherlike structures that are tightly packed together.

There are also worms which do not have fans, although some do have tentacles with which to feed. Others are actually very 'earthworm-like', and yet more have shapes which are quite bizarre – paper-thin, flattened bodies, for example.

In the marine environment, worms are specialised creatures filling discreet niches to which they are effectively adapted. It is possible to show only a few here, but even so some strange creatures, such as the reef building Organ-pipe Worm, are included and illustrate just how fascinating the inhabitants of the marine environment can be.

DOUBLE-SPIRAL WORM
Bispira volutacornis • Péist
dhébhíseach

These fan worms have a strong grey tube and are found in rocky areas – the tubes can usually be seen protruding from cracks or from between boulders. When disturbed the fan withdraws into the tube incredibly quickly leaving only a bare tube (often with a figure-of-eight opening showing).

A FANWORM • *Megalomma vesiculosum* **(Sabellidae)** • **(Feanphéist)**

Some worms protrude from their holes in sandy or muddy seabeds, with their fans extended into the water flow. They can disappear, almost instantly, into the seabed when threatened, as the one shown here (it has no common name) will do.

PEACOCK WORM • *Sabella pavonina* • **Péist phéacóige**

This worm has a long tube (up to 30 cm in length) formed from very fine particles, which protrudes from the seabed. From the end, the worm can extend a glorious, large and delicate feathery fan. Sometimes these worms, which also occur in the sand amongst seagrass, can be found in large numbers.

EYELASH WORM • *Myxicola infundibulum* • Péist fabhra

Although this worm lives in sand and mud, appearances can be deceptive, as they are here off Valentia Island, Co. Kerry. These worms are indeed living in mud, but the mud itself is coated in a layer of green seaweed, making it invisible.

Making Use of Iron

HORSESHOE WORM
Phoronis sp. – probably *hippocrepia* • Crú-phéist

These worms can bore into limestone and shells, eventually weakening them and thus allowing other boring creatures to start boring into them too. They can be found in extremely high numbers and, because individually they are small, they appear to coat rocks and shells with a very fine white 'fur'. Oddly enough, these phoronid worms have something in common with us as they use iron to transport oxygen around their bodies as we do. (Our blood uses haemoglobin, which contains iron, to perform the same function).

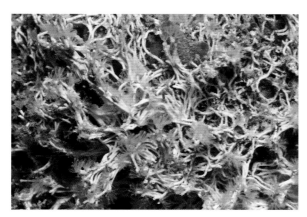

Whilst some worms bore into lime-rich rock others, like this coral worm, produce numerous small calcareous tubes.

Biogenic Worm Reefs

ORGAN-PIPE WORM or RED TUBE WORM
Serpula vermicularis • **Tiúbphéist dhearg**

Biogenic reefs are reefs formed from the hard parts of living things – the best known being the tropical coral reefs. In Irish waters the Organ-pipe Worm (which is a member of the serpulid worm family) is actually able to form small reefs that are known as Serpulid Worm Reefs.

This worm is a quite common and widespread marine creature that has a crown of vividly colourful, feathery tentacles. It produces a hard white tube in which to live, measuring several millimetres in diameter and up to tens of centimetres long. In suitable conditions large numbers of the hard tubes can form the basis of these reef structures. As the factors that make locations are unusual, the reefs are rare and are only known to exist in a few places on the west coasts of Ireland and Scotland.

Many other marine creatures find that these reefs offer them a home, with animals such as crabs taking shelter in crevices formed when some of the worms die off. Many other species live within the reefs too; squat lobsters, hermit crabs, starfish, sea squirts and sponges, as well as seaweeds and other small animals like anemones perching on top of the reefs.

Whilst the worms are able to retreat into their tubes for protection if they detect movement or changing light patterns, the reefs as a whole are actually very fragile and extremely susceptible to physical damage.

Long & Thin

A RIBBON WORM possibly *Nipponnemertes pulcher* (Nemertea) • (Péist neimirtíneach)

Ribbon worms can be extremely long and thin. Some can be as long as 5 to 10 m. They are carnivores and some are known to prey on crustaceans. When this one was first seen it appeared to be feeding on a dead prawn, but whether it had caught the prawn or simply found a dead one is not known.

This orange ribbon worm was photographed at night in Lough Hyne, Co. Cork, and it is difficult to be absolutely certain of its identity. Although they can be quite abundant, ribbon worms are seldom seen because they often bury in sand or mud and may, like this one, come out to feed at night. Few scientists specialise in research into Nemertean worms like this one, so they are understudied and little is known about them.

Soft & Fragile

STRAWBERRY WORM
***Eupolymnia nebulosa* • Péist ghalabanach**

The Strawberry Worm is one of the Irish spaghetti worms and is found throughout Europe. Strawberry worms build themselves tubes out of sand and gravel fragments, which they cement together; these usually remain buried, with the worms inside. Although these worms usually prefer to live on a sandy or muddy seabed, for some reason this one is out on the surface of some maerl and so it is possible to see its soft and very vulnerable pink body and the numerous long feeding tentacles.

CANDY-STRIPE FLATWORM • *Prostheceraeus vittatus* • Leithphéist stríoca candaí

This flatworm is so thin that it sometimes appears to 'flow' over the surface over which it is travelling. It is a very distinctive and not uncommon animal, with its dark stripes and brighter body edge. It can often be seen eating Light-bulb Sea Squirts (see page 116).

Plant Life

In the sea, as on land, plants need light in order to live. Seawater absorbs light quickly and by a depth of about 10 m virtually all the red light has gone. In the clearest of seas, light can only penetrate a few hundred metres down and beyond a depth of 200 m there is very little light left. In temperate waters, like those surrounding Ireland, light penetration is usually just a few tens of metres. Few plants exist beyond this depth and so they are mostly confined to relatively shallow water. In shallow water, however, plants can be extremely abundant. In fact, kelp plants form so called 'forests' where the plants grow profusely and so-close together that it can be a struggle for a diver to clamber through them.

Plant life in the sea is incredibly varied. Whilst kelps are strong and resilient, smaller seaweeds can be delicate, almost filigree affairs, giving the impression that they would not survive the rough and tumble of wave action. There are seaweeds that have floats to allow them to hang vertically in the water when the tide covers them, whilst others have hard, brittle, calcareous skeletons. Some merely form a thin pink crust over the rock's surface.

On the shore, rockpools are often filled with curiously-shaped plants of green, red and brown, and seaweed-covered rocky shores can be a slippery nightmare to walk on.

Seagrass, unlike seaweeds, is a flowering plant. It forms shallow meadows which give the impression of being wafted by a slow-motion underwater breeze, as its blades sway to and fro in rhythm with the waves above them.

CONSTANTLY-MOVING KELP

Plants which live in a continuously-moving and powerful medium like seawater have to be tough. Kelp plants are leathery and rubbery and are able to withstand immense battering. Even so, winter gales and storm conditions mean many kelp plants will eventually be ripped from their anchorages and washed up onto beaches.

Small Worlds

ROCKPOOLS

High on the shore

A rockpool high up on the shore will contain plant (and animal) species able to survive without the need for a dousing of fresh seawater for nearly a whole tidal cycle. As such pools can become very warm on a hot day (or may even contain ice during a very cold winter), their inhabitants need to be very tolerant of temperature changes. They also need to be able to withstand changes in the salt content of the pools, which can be reduced by rain or increased by evaporation on hot days. Oxygen levels will also drop as the pool's inhabitants use it up, and will also vary depending on both temperature and the length of time between low and high tides.

Perhaps surprisingly, when the tide is out seaweeds attract other creatures including Seaweed Flies.

The view from below

Rockpools are small worlds in themselves. This one, which lies halfway up a rocky shore, contains a mix of plants able to tolerate the living conditions specific to a rockpool in this part of the shore. Bootlace Weed and Green Gut Weed, together with Tuning Fork Weed, can all be seen here.

A Secret Garden

SEA BEECH & EYELASH WEED
Delesseria sanguinea & Calliblepharis ciliata •
Feá mara & Lus fabhra

Red seaweeds flourish in shallow water, and where the kelp is not too densely packed they can form an exquisite undersea garden. Sea Beech, with its veined, leaf-like fronds and the flat blades of Eyelash Weed provide a glorious under-storey to the tree-like kelp. None of them is ever still, constantly swaying and swirling in the undersea current.

Most seaweeds look their best in spring and early summer, but as the year progresses they start to die off and become increasingly shabby-looking. As the sea breaks them up, water visibility decreases due to the multitude of seaweed particles floating around.

Rock Garden

DIVIDED NET-WEED & BONNEMAISON'S FERN WEED
Dictyota dichotoma & Bonnemaisonia asparagoides •
Lus ladhrach & Asparagach Bonnemaison

Rock surfaces can be entirely covered by contrastingly-coloured and shaped seaweeds. Here the khaki, forked and ribbon-like fronds of Divided Net-weed are adjacent to the delicately-branched and almost luminous pink Bonnemaison's Fern Weed.

Like land plants, seaweeds can be pressed and dried. Pressed specimens are kept as records in Sherkin Island Marine Station's herbarium.

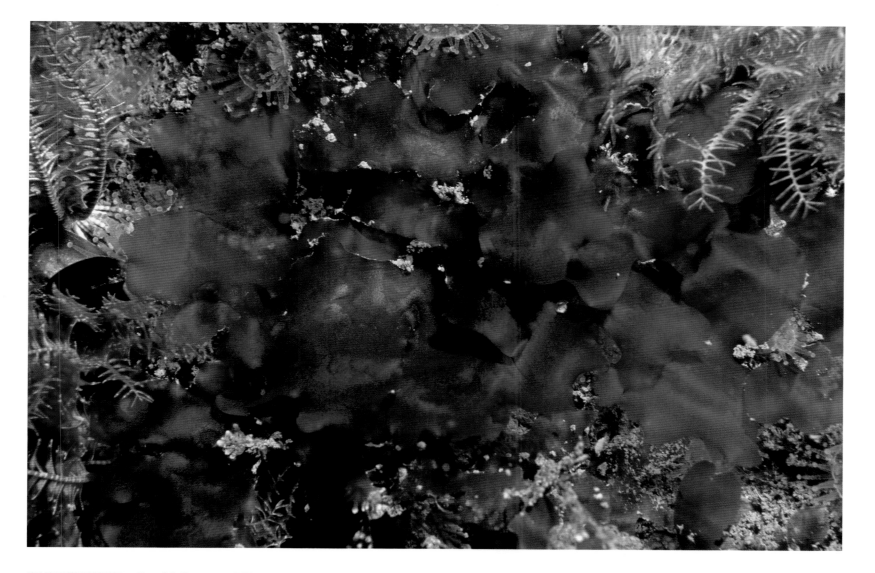

RAINBOW WEED • *Drachiella spectabilis* • Lus dea-dhathach

This seaweed really does have vivid iridescent colouration on its fronds. It is found on rocky seabeds, usually gently sloping ones, down to a depth of about 20 m where there is good, clear water.

Marine Meadows

SEAGRASS or EELGRASS
Zostera marina • **Miléarach**

Snakelocks anemones (*Anemonia viridis*) are shallow-water-dwelling anemones, which often climb seaweeds to get closer to the light (see page 23). They are frequently abundant in seagrass beds, where they can climb the sturdy blades.

Seagrass blades do not look unlike those of grasses found above water and it is the only flowering plant found in Irish seas. Its roots help to stabilise the sand in which it needs to grow and it survives only in places where there is a degree of shelter and adequate light. When conditions are suitable though, it can form large undersea meadows.

Seagrasses are in decline internationally and this is a cause for concern because they provide an important and sheltered habitat for many other plants and animals. As seagrass stabilizes the sandy seabed in which it lives, large areas of seagrass can help protect coasts from erosion and so it is considered to be a very important marine plant.

This meadow illustrates how seagrass can transform what might otherwise be bare sand into a rich habitat, filled with many other plants and animals. It shows anemones living on the blades, sea lettuce mixed in with the seagrass, as well as other, smaller seaweeds growing on the plants.

Sculpted Bedrock

PLANTS AS A THIN COVERING

Some seaweeds form a thin pink crust on suitable rocky surfaces. This photograph shows a gully off Sherkin Island, Co. Cork, which has been worn into its present shape by the action of boulders and cobbles (see bottom of picture), being moved about in it by the sea over a long period of time. In summer it is covered in thin animal and plant crusts, some of which will be worn off during autumnal and winter gales.

The pink is an encrusting calcareous seaweed which is very thin but also pretty tough as it has to survive in conditions which even in summer can be fairly harsh. Larger seaweeds can be seen growing higher up the steeply-sloping rock.

ENCRUSTING SEAWEED

The pink encrustation shown here is one of a number of seaweeds which form thin calcareous crusts over rock. These are very tough plants and can withstand substantial physical hardships. Other crusts can be formed by animals and even by lichens.

Plant Skeletons

MAERL
probably *Phymatolithon calcareum* • Maerla

There are several species of free-living, coralline algae in Ireland which are collectively known as maerl. These strange plants are very slow-growing but can be found covering quite extensive areas where the coarse nature of the seabed that they form supports a large number of other animals, many of which can dig into it in order to hide.

The most common maerl is in a twiggy form as shown here, but other species produce different shapes. Some even produce 'nodules', which may be as much as a hundred years old or more.

'Coral' Strand

When maerl dies it loses its colour. In areas where it is abundant and close inshore the dead maerl is often swept up onto the shore and, together with broken shells, can form a substantial part of the beach material. When it does so, the white beach is often referred to as a 'coral' strand, despite the maerl being of plant origin and quite unlike true corals, which are the remains of animals.

ABOVE THE KELP FOREST

Kelp plants are extremely strong and tough, as any large plants might be expected to be in order to endure the constant and none-too-gentle caresses of the sea around the Irish coast. From above, kelp forests show only their thick canopy of large and heavy leaf-like fronds.

KELP FROM BELOW

From below, it becomes clear that the numerous kelp plants need rock on which to gain a grip with their root-like 'holdfasts'. They do not actually have roots but these 'holdfasts' hold onto the rock like distorted hands, with numerous, strangely-shaped fingers.

On the Edge

*I*reland lies on the western fringe of Europe, jutting far out into the Atlantic Ocean from mainland Europe. In terms of its location, it is unique. Its coastline is also very varied, which means that it offers numerous habitats to a huge diversity of marine species. Just a few of these species can be seen from above water. These include seals, dolphins, porpoises, basking sharks and very rarely whales and turtles, although the last three are unusual sights.

Ireland's coastline is also incredibly beautiful, and this beauty is accentuated by the highly changeable weather systems, which rapidly move in from the open ocean. These weather systems dramatically affect the scene both above and below water. Calm seas allow any suspended material to settle and the water can become very clear. Off the west coast water clarity can, on occasion, rival that in the tropics. In winter, storms stir up everything and the sea becomes murky, with no visibility whatsoever.

In between are 'normal conditions' with constant motion in the water from swells, waves, tidal and other currents. Underwater visibility varies, as do the changing forces acting on the coast, the shallow seabeds and their inhabitants.

Living by the sea has always been a tough existence. Man has adapted both his tools and the land to survive by the coast, just like the marine plants and animals have themselves adapted to live and flourish in extremely challenging conditions.

An early evening view over Roaringwater Bay

Sherkin Island is positioned so that the northern coasts offer views to the north and west over the other islands and mainland Co. Cork. This view from the Marine Station is almost timeless.

COMMON SEAL • *Phoca vitulina* • Rón beag

This young Common Seal was sitting next to one of the large rockpools on the rocky seashore at Kilkee, Co. Clare. Seals are probably the largest marine mammal that most people see, as dolphins and whales (cetaceans) are far less common close inshore.

Pure Power

BOTTLE-NOSED DOLPHIN
Tursiops truncatus • **Deilf bholgshrónach**

A large Bottle-nosed Dolphin like 'Fungi' is a spectacular sight when leaping out of the sea. This behaviour – known as 'breaching' – shows just how strong these animals are, as it takes a tremendous amount of power and energy to launch such a large creature out of the water. To be able leap entirely clear of it is quite astonishing.

As Close as Possible

Dolphins which attach themselves to a particular location (as 'Fungi' – the 'Dingle Dolphin' has done in the sea near Dingle, Co. Kerry), offer a rare opportunity for many to see and even get close to these intriguing animals. Such dolphins attract a great deal of attention and publicity and can even become a tourist attraction.

STORMY SUNSET FROM FENIT

The Atlantic Ocean dominates the west of Ireland. Fast-changing weather systems sweep in from the open sea and provide some very dramatic and spectacular backdrops over the ceaseless ocean, especially when they coincide with the setting sun.

HUGE ATLANTIC WAVES

The Aran Islands, off the west coast of Ireland, feel the power of Atlantic swells, with massive walls of water battering their exposed coasts. This is not a coastline to be explored by the unwary as it is all too easy to be caught out by one of the occasional larger swells.

The Worm Hole – Poll na bPéist

A visit to the unique natural swimming pool on the westward-facing coast of the Aran Island of Inis Mór can be a most surreal experience for divers on a very calm day. Invisible from the surface is an undersea tunnel which connects the open sea with the pool and which divers are occasionally able to swim through before surfacing inside this disconcertingly regular, kelp-fringed pool.

The enormous power of Atlantic storms has removed a huge block of limestone from the sloping rocky shore. The resulting massive 'rockpool' is known as the Worm Hole (Poll na bPéist); its Gaelic name refers to an ancient mythological monster from the deep.

KELP BELOW THE SURFACE

It is very rare for the sea to be absolutely still. Even on the calmest of days, there is almost always sufficient movement to stir up the top layer of water and continuously swirl plants around in a flurry of bubbles.

A VAST KELP-LINED POOL

In sheltered places, and on a calm day, it can still require a descent to several metres of depth to attain any degree of stillness in the undersea world. This photo shows some of the calmest of conditions. Looking upwards, shimmering clouds are visible through the water's lightly-rippled surface.

A storm in 1960 wrecked the "Plassey" and another bad storm shortly afterwards washed her high up on the shoreline of Inis Oírr in the Aran Islands. Beyond the reach of all but the severest weather, she survives as a rusting hulk and is now something of a tourist attraction.

The Destructive Power of the Sea

Wrecks are rare on Ireland's west coast. Those ships which get into trouble do not survive as wrecks for long. The powerful Atlantic waves and swell, and the winter gales flatten any vessel which strikes the shore, and it soon becomes an unrecognisable jumble of rusty plates and twisted girders. Few marine creatures live on such wrecks until they are completely smashed and are assimilated into the seabed.

The container ship "Ranga" came to grief at Dunmore Head on the Dingle Peninsula in 1982. She quickly broke up, with the superstructure surviving the longest.

Although it may be hard to believe from a summer photograph taken in calm weather, Atlantic gales pounded the "Ranga", breaking pieces off her, and eventually pushed the large remaining section over and into the cliffs. Much was eventually salvaged and the sea relentlessly destroyed the rest.

Visible Vegetation

SEAWEED-DOMINATED SHORE

The sheltered side of the Aran Islands can offer seaweeds the chance to settle on the gently shelving rocky shore. In near-perfect conditions like this, the seaweeds dominate and almost entirely cover the rocks. They also dominate the shallow rockpools that have formed through the erosion of the limestone.

On the shore, boulders offer a good, stable surface for seaweeds to grow on and can easily disappear under a luxuriant coating of plant life.

SANDY BEACHES

The county of Mayo has some fine beaches with just a few boulders, cobbles, pebbles and peat showing through the sand. Seaweeds coat the harder rock surfaces wherever they are able to, but cannot survive on the softer sand or peat.

LIVING WITH THE SEA

The ceaseless pounding of the Atlantic grinds up rock and has provided numerous building-blocks for use by those who lived along its shores in the past. Agricultural land is sometimes protected right down to the sea by drystone walls constructed from stones from the beaches.

Landscape Features

SUPPLIES FROM THE SEA

Small drystone-walled fields are characteristic of the Aran Islands. The islanders filled these fields with seaweed and kelp which eventually rotted and produced soil. The fields were kept small in order to prevent the seaweed and kelp from being blown away, and this has created the patchwork landscape of tiny fields that we see today.

Small fields and years of fertilisation by seaweeds have dramatically altered the Aran Islands forever.

SUNSET FROM SHERKIN ISLAND

The Marine Station's landing stage offers an amazing westerly view, which only becomes all the more glorious as the sun sinks and finally sets over the Calf Islands and Mount Gabriel.

SUNSET OVER DUBLIN

Perhaps one of the most poignant memories I have of leaving Ireland is from many years ago when I watched a priest take out his white cotton handkerchief to wave goodbye as he left on the ferry. The sunset was timed to perfection and slipped swiftly away as the ferry headed out to sea.

Index

ENGLISH NAMES

SCIENTIFIC NAMES

IRISH NAMES